David Mason has worked as an immunopathologist, a sales training manager and has owned a restaurant. He began writing in 1993; his first book was produced in 1996. He works in schools teaching children how to be terribly dramatic and write stories and poems. He has six wonderful children and a lovely wife. They live in Norfolk in a happy, noisy house.

WITHDRAWN FOR SALE

"Wild!" © David J. Mason 2009
Publishing address: North Street Publishing
1 Millfield Road, North Walsham, Norfolk NR28 0EB
Telephone: 01692 406877   www.InspireToWrite.co.uk
Email: DavidMasonPoet@AOL.com

Cover illustration from www.BigStockPhoto.com

British Library Cataloguing-in-Publication Data
A catalogue record for this book is available from the British Library
David J. Mason
ISBN 978-0-9558898-5-1

All rights reserved. No part of this book may be reproduced or utilised in any form or by any means, electronic or mechanical, including photocopying, recording, or by any information storage and retrieval system without permission in writing from the Publisher.

By the same author:

"Inside Out"	Poetry 1996
"Speaking Out"	Audio collection 1997
"Get a Life"	Poetry 1997; illustrations by Nick Walmsley
"Seven Summers"	Poetry 1998
"Leo's Magic Shoes"	Children's novel 1999; illustrations by Kirsty Munro. Reprinted in 2000 as "Pedro's Magic Shoes" with illustrations by Nick Walmsley
"The Great Sweetshop Robbery"	Children's poetry 2001
"Handy Andy has the Candy"	Children's poetry 2001
"Go Teddy Go"	Children's CD poetry-songs 2002
"After Midnight"	Children's novel 2003 amended and re-released as "Midnight Mystery" 2009
"The Elf who sang the King to sleep"	Children's fables and fairy tales 2002 Reprinted 2009
"Living in another world"	Children's poetry 2003
"Teacher's Cauldron"	Children's poetry 2004
"When…"	Children's poetry 2005
"Two into one"	Children's poetry 2006 Reprinted 2008 (twice)
"The White Book"	Children's poetry 2006
"Learning to Fly"	Children's novel 2007
"Metaphor Man"	Children's poetry 2008
"Signing On"	Adult poetry collection 2008
"Midnight Mystery"	Children's adventure novel 2009

Printed by JEM Digital Print Services Ltd
Staplehurst Road, Sittingbourne, Kent ME10 2NH
www.jem.co.uk

NORFOLK LIBRARY AND
INFORMATION SERVICE

SUPP	Inspire to write	2
INV.NO.	NON1095	
ORD DATE	19.5.10	

Contents

Teacher Creature 6

A Home for everyone? 8

Lonely Goalposts 10

Nice, but cold 11

Announcement 12

Pass it, here! 13

The Power of Speech 14

Time Travel 16

The Colours of Creation 17

Something to think about 18

Crash Landing 19

Chalk and Cheese 20

Inspiration 22

War of Words 24

The Teaching Forecast 26

Geography Lesson 27

Getting even 28

When Ofsted comes to Town 29

Your School is not my Game 30

Mood Change 31

The Sound of Silence 32

Down at Le Hedge Priv-ay 33

Wild! 34

The jolly Farmer 36

Down at the Farm 37

Pet without a Name 38

Sunset 39

I'm the Sun! 40

Red Sky at Night 42

Some dogs do Poetry 43

A little hard to swallow 44

Talking Books 45
Sums 46
Badly equipped 51
The Poet who painted his Toenails red 52
Writing can be hard Work 54
When I am away (for all my children) 55
The Real World 56
First Day 58
Time 60
Barcelona vs. Manchester United 62
Penalty-taker 63
Super Striker slays Gloomy Goalie 64
Plasters 66
Only a Game 68
Watersliding for Professionals 69
Cool Dip 70
My Dad's bigger than yours 71
Beards 72
Fooling God 73
Fishing for the Truth 75
The Lady and the Dog 77
Ice Cubes 78
Make up your Mind 79
Dressing up 80
Nod and Don 81
Dog and God 82
Ghost Train 83
Oh! Tea! (Nana's rap) 86
Pedestrians, where are you? 88
Sock Fluff 90
The Return of the Chocolate Biscuit 91
Poet's Revenge 94

Wild!

Teacher Creature

Delivered by the headmaster
Wrapped up tight in a dark box
It appeared to be our new teacher
Who came with instructions and was made in China.

Congratulations on your choice of teacher.
(We didn't want him in the first place)
Your teacher has been built
To last a lifetime.
(Oh no! Looks like he's here to stay)
Careful attention to detail
Will ensure your teacher functions
Efficiently over the years.
Please consider the following:

Your teacher is not a toy.
Never sit or stand on your teacher.
Always keep hands out of moving parts.
For indoor use only
In a supervised classroom.
Protect from severe weather conditions.
Not to be used by more
Than thirty pupils at once.
Switch off mobile phones during operation
As these may interfere with the relay mechanism.

Replace batteries or recharge
At regular intervals.
Check tea/coffee* levels frequently.

Repairs must only be carried out
By qualified persons.

Finally, remember your teacher
Is only a machine
And may malfunction
From time to time
Especially after heavy usage.
This is quite normal
And cooling of overheated parts
During school recess
Should bring your teacher back
To full operating capacity.

Now, sit back, switch on
And enjoy.....

*Depends on the model

A Home for everyone?

Some such as sultans
Have many, many homes.
Others like celebrities
Must make do with some.
Most people, lucky people
Just have one
And can you believe it?
Some have none.

Some palatial, grand
Others rather tall
Some on middle ground
And others weeny small
And, yes you've guessed it
Some no size at all.

Some are made of marble
Others precious stone
Most are bricks and mortar
A few are mud and straw
Others in the gutters
Are fashioned in cardboard.

Some are worth a million
Others not so much
But every home is valued
Every owner rich
Except for those who haven't one,
A home to call their own
And sleep on streets still paved with gold
That's chilling to the bone.

Lonely Goalposts

In the fluttering winter light
A seasonal gloom calls time
On crippled posts sunk
In yesteryear's glorious goalmouth mud.
Where teams fought tooth and nail
To force the ball down a gaping throat
Feeding greedily on the thrill –
But now choking in harmony
With rasping breaths of a chilling north-easterly.

Lonely goalposts on last legs
Await the penalty for their neglect,
Council summons the red card which
Removes them from their tired pitch.

Nice, but cold

Sand hints of treasure
Sky whispers pleasure
Waves say exciting
Sea calls inviting
Summer beach shouts out fun
Tourists frozen solid cry
Where's the sun?

Announcement

This is an announcement from
School Control Central:
Please take care when leaving
Inattentive pupils in the classroom.
All inattentive pupils will be
Removed and placed in the playground.
All thirty of us, pens down
Sleepwalked outside without a sound.

Pass it, here!

Here, here, over here!
Pass the ball, pass the ball
It's me here!
Pass the ball, pass the ball
I'm in space!
Pass the ball, pass the ball
There's no one here at all
Pass the ball, pass the ball
I'm bound to score a goal
Pass the ball, pass the ball
I'm not offside!
Pass the ball – oh alright
Sorry I didn't realise
You're on the other side.

The Power of Speech

Caterpillar crawled across his nettle bed
Munching idly as he went
When Butterfly fluttered overhead
And observing young Caterpillar said
I remember those days
So, so far away
Or so to me it seems
When, like you, I lived life's young dreams.
(Here Caterpillar continued to nibble
Not giving a nasturtium leaf for the old man's
drivel)

Ah yes! sighed Butterfly
The days when time drifts slowly by
O'er leaves that taste so sweet and crisp
(Here Butterfly licked those elegant lips)
But now there's only nectar to sip.
Caterpillar nodded and chewed some more
And tried to ignore this butterfly bore.

You should stop, he started again
And think what a wonder it is to be young
Change the odd skin is all you've to do
No bother with fashions or patterns for you.
Yes, you'll learn, that's all about to change
It's all about appearances, attracting a mate
Making sure those eggs are laid
To keep on running that caterpillar race.

Blah, blah, blah, blah, blah, blah, blah,
Droned Butterfly to Caterpillar.

Caterpillar yawned and turned away dismissive
And Caterpillar – by now bored rigid
Gave up the ghost and turned into a chrysalis.

Time Travel

Watching the clock slow turning
I felt a real burning
Desire to fly through time
So clasped the hands
Of the clock in mine
And in the minutes
And hours that followed
Flew through a future hollow
To see what it promised
This bright new tomorrow
But as the clock
Struck midnight
I let go the hands
And fell through the sands
Of time
And resting now upon my bed
Is time a place inside my head?

The Colours of Creation

The countryside a carpet
Of all shades of green
From the dark to the lightest
And a range in between.
God charged the angels and
Said 'Keep it clean'
But their muddy brown boots
Made the bark of the trees
And their filthy black mitts
The branches and twigs.
God said to the angels
'A mess you have made
First it was green
Now every brown shade
But I like the mix
It looks rather grand,
The pattern's fantastic
Though not as I'd planned
And what shall we do with
The pure blue sea?'
The angels replied
'Paint it turquoise and green.'

Something to think about

You're never more
Than ten metres
From a rat –
A scientific fact.
I stand in the middle
Of a chalk circle
(Ten metres diameter)

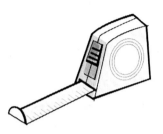

Armed with a loaded pistol.
Sure enough he appears
And casually stares.
Incensed I aim
Between those beady eyes.
Bang! At the black
He dies, but as he does
So smiles.
I know then
I cannot rest.
Agitated, I scan
My circumference.
He knew I had not won
That there is another one
Just twenty metres further on
From where I stand.
And that rat
Is a living, breathing
Mathematical fact.

Crash Landing

Last night an emperor moth
Fell from the dark skies
Above southern France
Following engine failure.
The crash investigators
Noted a damaged wing
Possibly sustained during crash landing
On the toilet floor
Of the sanitary block.
Emperor surprised animal hospital
By taking to the skies once more
Following a simple draught of honey –
But with plenty
Of his fellows elegantly
Gliding through the deep night
You are strongly advised
Not to visit the toilet
During the early hours of
The morning, when without warning
You may be struck
By the wreckage
From this king of the skies
Whose insignia bold
Is the sight of four eyes.

Chalk and Cheese

It was with great regret
We discovered too late
The moon was made of cheese
For astronauts from rocket ships
Had eaten most of it.
Now no more than a sliver
This finger nail silver
Hung in the sky
Till alien mice
Did nibble the remainder.

And now the sea is fretting
It doesn't know what to do
It's neither in nor out
Since the moon gave up its pull.
It's hanging round the middle
Its waves are rather small
Without the moon to help it
It's not a sea at all.

The dark is oh so dark!
Without the orb a-shining
And no one will go out at night
Without the moon to guide them
And now there are no lunatics

And no men in the moon
And where are all the werewolves
Who come out when it's full?

You know we need the moon again
To fill that giant space.
The stars are two a-penny
The moon a special case.
They say they're going to build one
You know, I've heard the talk.
To make sure no one eats it,
They'll make the moon from chalk.

Inspiration

The teacher gave me the idea for a po-em
I can tell straight away that it is a dead one
I can see by lookin' right at it
I won't be able to write about it.
I breathe a sigh in utter frustration
Try mouth to mouth resuscitation
But man! This poem he won't breathe
This poem's just starin' back at me
(Starin' back at me... starin' back at me).

What, I ask myself, is my problem?
I got a brain and somethin' to write on
But I'm sittin' here in exasperation
Doin' too much of that exhalation
I need some negotiation
Get me some angels, a delegation
Try me some heavenly levitation
Summon the help of the God of Creation
Say Lord ain't I go no imagination?
No what I don't have is inspiration.
(No inspiration, no inspiration).

Do you have inspiration?
What is it you need?
I tell you inspiration
It's a tiny little seed
That grows from deep inside your mind
And flowers my oh my!
And the things you do, well I say ooh!
Like fireworks in the sky.

Yeah, yeah, yeah! Inspiration.
Yeah, yeah, yeah! And I'm waitin'.
Yeah, yeah, yeah! I'm impatient.
Yeah, yeah, yeah! Exploration.
Yeah, yeah, yeah! Communication.
Yeah, yeah, yeah! Congratulation.
Yeah, yeah, yeah! Exultation.
Yeah, yeah, yeah! Here's salvation!
Yeah, yeah, yeah! Inspiration!

Inspiration, inspiration, inspiration!

War of Words

Johnny don't be scared of the page
But the blank is a minefield
And the pen a grenade.
Teacher took the pin out, shout!
Johnny run and don't look back.
Over the top where you mind is lost
In a cold expanse of drowning fog.

Johnny falters towards the line
There's a nagging doubt
In the black of his mind.
Concentrate on the job in hand!
He steels himself and takes the pen
And dares the enemy, show yourself.

Johnny stares into that milky distance
And clutches for his own existence
Out of reach of those bullet points
Like hail sprayed from the voiceless void
Orders the troops to an all-out assault
But Johnny he never agreed to sign up.

Johnny's gun is firing blanks
Stops dead alone in no man's land.
Questions why they signed him up
Turns his back and away he runs
From the bombs that blast inside his head
Bu we know they shoot deserters, my friend.

The Teaching Forecast
(A poem for teachers all at sea)

This is the teaching forecast
Issued at 0800 hours GMT
Today, Wednesday September 5th.
There are warnings of lows
Approaching in all areas.
0900 hours pressure rising
In all classrooms.
Teachers veering into staffroom.
Jordan, Connor and Kylie
Daft becoming moronic.
1200 hours gales increasing
To storm force in playground
By 1300 hours – not good.
1400 hours P.E.
Showers. Pupils moderate or good
But becoming variable.
Staff backtracking into stock room.
Visibility poor, falling (over).
Clearing 1500 hours.
Highs expected.
One or two down the bars.

Geography Lesson

Imagine the rain falling
High up in the mountains.
Somewhere the water pools,
Finds a crack, begins to flow.
The river's beginning
Is called the source
Which it licks from tomato
Rocks of course.

Getting even

All the even numbers said
To the rest of them
You're a bit odd
Aren't you?
You can't be halved
To make a whole
You're all point fives
The lot of you.
The odds replied,
Well, double us
You'll see what we can do
And now we're not
The slightest bit odd
No, we've got even with you.

When Ofsted comes to Town

When Ofsted comes to town
We're gonna dance in the playground!
Gonna sing Hallelujah!
Prove it to yer!
Won't know what's hit yer
You'll be so impressed yeah!
Paint up the walls
And shine up your shoes yeah!
When Ofsted comes to
When Ofsted comes to
When Ofsted comes to town.

Your School is not my Game

I'm in assembly, look straight ahead
And make sure I'm blinking.
Move my lips in all the right bits
To make it look like I'm singing.
I don't draw attention
By fussing or fidgeting
False fingers in my ears
The silence is deafening.
And now I'm in the dressing
Room or on the subs' bench waiting
And like a lot of time in school
I'm not actually playing
The game they think I am.
Instead I'm dreaming up another one
And like so many kids around me
Sidelined, I'm waiting to come on.

Mood Change

Wake one day
To the wild wind howling
And a mad sea roaring
A thunderous booming
Lightning blinding.
The storm though is passing
A dark night ending
Moon bathes in silver, sinking.

A new dawn is coming
The sun strokes syrup gold loving
Clouds carry me away
Wrapped in warmest wool
Silent sleeping, tummy full.

The Sound of Silence

Beyond the heartbeat,
The pulsing of sap
Through the tubes of the tree
And the rustling of its leaves.
The song of the birds
And the murmur of the breeze.
Everything moving underground
Or crawling on the surface
Or flying makes no sound.
Not even a mood,
The shouts for joy
Or the moans of sadness,
A very nothingness,
Where nothing
Not a thing
Stirs
And all those bits
Of our brains well-oiled
Whirr and whirr.

Down at Le Hedge Priv-ay

It's a private club
At the privet hedge
This place is buzzin'
Bees jumpin' balancin'
On del-i-cate branches
Hoppin' from one sweet
Flower to another,
Knockin' back nectar.
Dancin' a fig-ure eight
All day long.
Puttin' away protein packed
Packets of pollen
And hoverin' under
That noon day sun.
This here's the bee all
To end all.
There's no flies on them.
Down at *Le Hedge Privét*
The private club – for bees on-ly...

Wild!

Watch out! All you
Hikers and cyclers
Lovers of the outdoor lifers,
There are wild
Flowers in the countryside –
Us buttercups and daisies
All sorts of crazies
Of every kind
In this countryside.

Dancing flowers, waving flowers,
Clap-hap-happy flowers,With nectar brimming
flowers.
Golden sunny
Sweet as honey flowers,
Forest flavoured
Heaven scented flowers.
Red, white
A few electric blue flowers,
Hullaballoo, forget-me-not and
How-do-you-do? flowers.
A range of strange flowers
Lurking, working away flowers –
Empowered flowers.
Creeping through field

Walking through woodland flowers
Spreading and treading towards
The city's door flowers.

There are the dull flowers –
Towny flowers.
Ordinary green and browny flowers,
Prim and proper all
Grown up and older flowers.
Guarded, standing straight
Tame and all the same flowers,
All ashamed because they'd
Like to be game –
Instead of meek and mild
Who need to get a life – flowers.

And our living
Begs a question –
Where are we growing
In God's garden?

The jolly Farmer

The jolly farmer opened his window
And scanned the rows of new potatoes.
He swore he heard a moaning sound
From his crop where it lay, right there in the
ground.
He did! He heard it again and again
But why should a bunch of potatoes complain?
The jolly farmer: he scoured his brain.
'Oh, aye!' he said. "Tis growing pains!'

Down at the Farm

Pig in the sty says Oink
Cow in the shed says Moo
Stabled horse says Neigh
Kennelled dog says Woof.

Sheep in field says Baa
Organically Certified
Free Range Chicken
Says OK Ya.

Pet without a Name

I have a cat called Tabby
And a piebald horse
A dog named Spot
And a patchwork mouse,
A cheetah known as Measles
A zebra – she's Stripe
And another
Same colour
All over
White
And I don't call him
Anything.

Sunset

It was time for bed
The sun was bright red
And embarrassed to be caught undressed
Or more likely in her nightie
When whispering streets of clouds soft
Told the whole of Heaven the mystery.
I looked long
Enough to realise.
It made my eyes
Sore to spy on her
So turned away
For a moment or two
To see the pale moon rising instead
And when I sneaked another peek
Found she had gone to bed
On that mattress –
The horizon
And I'd have to wait to see her
Properly dressed
The following morning.

I'm the Sun!

I woke up in the morning
The cloud it filled the sky
None of you could see me
I was hiding up on high.
The grey wall all around me
I tried to shine on through
But you people have to help me
And turn the black to blue.

Chorus:

> *I'm the sun*
> *I'm the sun*
> *Come on everyone!*
> *How about having*
> *Some fun in the sun?*
> *I'm the sun*
> *I'm the sun*
> *Come on everyone!*
> *It's time to start playing*
> *All the work's been done.*

A happy heart can do it
A smile on the face
No furrowed brow or downturned mouth
This world's a better place.
I know that you can do it
Just concentrate to find
The clear blue corners up above
That dwell within your mind.

Chorus

Think about the good things
You have them all for free
The mountains and the valleys
The rivers and the seas.
You smell and see, hear and touch
The wonders all around.
Why go looking for the treasure
That you've already found?

Chorus

Red Sky at Night

Wisps of shallow grey lay
Streaked across the
Deep blue backwash
Of shy old sky,
His face, wise,
Reflecting in the sunset fire.
Looking to the last flames
He kneels to contemplate
Another new day
A few dark hours sleep away,
But remembering the saying
He rubs old hands
At such a sight –
The promise of
Another shepherd's delight.

Some dogs do Poetry

I'm minding my own business
Writing some interesting poetry
When this nosy dog
Comes sniffing up to me
Biscuit crumbs on my paper
He leaves a silvery
Trail of doggy slobber
From the middle to the corner.
I can't read this,
I complain to the owner.
He's not listening
And the dog
He's too busy in the bushes
Writing another.

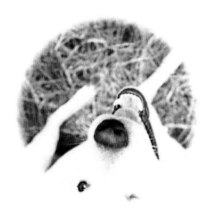

A little hard to swallow

It is assembly.
All the little ones are too well-behaved
And sit like rows of little flowers
In neat beds
Whilst the cloudy words of the adults
Float above their flower heads.
All the middle ones understand some
But shift uneasily at their lack of freedom
And the wisest of words can never take root
Under jiffling bottoms and Velcro-clad foot.
All the older ones understand it all
Far too well.
A few leave their faces switched on.
Some don't bother
And have travelled to another
Land where other
Things are going on undercover
Far beyond the headmaster's knowledge
Whose message, like cold lumpy porridge,
Is a little too hard to swallow.

Talking Books

Leafing through the pages
I couldn't decide
Until I heard the voice
That made up my mind.
'Do you read me?'
The book enquired.
Eager to please
And feeling inspired
I answered,
'Loud and clear, go ahead.'
But the book it was silent
As the words spoke for themselves.

Sums

I have this chocolate bar.
It has twenty-four pieces –
That's a lot of pieces –
Twenty-four to be precise.
I could do an awful
Lot with this bar.
Hmm, now let me see:

If I have twenty-four friends
I could give them all
A piece each
And being very generous
I could be chocolate-less.
But I don't have twenty-four friends.

And I'd like at least
One piece myself.
But twenty-three is a prime number
And I've never understood them,
Except I know you can't
Share a prime number
So I should give all twenty-three
To just one brilliant friend of mine.
But I haven't got a brilliant friend,
Not that brilliant anyway.

I like the number six
It has a nice curvy shape
It's actually my favourite.
So what I could do
Is divide twenty-four by six
Or even twenty-four by four
Giving six as the answer,
Or four, depending upon
Which number I divide by
In the beginning.
I think I'd choose to
Divide by four
Because I've only got
Three brilliant friends –
And me of course
Who I count as one
Of my best friends,
Probably my best one.

Right, so far so good.
I think I'd advise
My friends not to eat
All their chocolate at once.
They could divide their six
By the number of hours in
A day which would give them
A quarter of a piece of chocolate

Every hour if they didn't
Bother to sleep
Or if they wanted to keep
Their chocolate for a whole week
They could eat one piece a day
For the next six days
And then fast on the seventh.

I don't know what I'd do
With my six pieces of chocolate,
It's not that much come to think of it.
Knowing me I'd eat it all
Very quickly in one go
Probably in one big mouthful.

So on second thoughts I'd
Need more than six pieces.
It will still be very kind
Hearted of me to give away
Half of my chocolate.
And if I choose my two
Best friends instead of four
They could still have six bits each.
Knowing my appetite though
I doubt twelve pieces would
Be enough for me
So I think

I will choose eighteen
Which is still a multiple of six
And the remainder
Can be divided by two
To give three pieces each
To those two brilliant friends.

Now I'm thinking again.
I can't help it – it's my
Mathematical brain.
Supposing there's an emergency.
I'll need an extra three pieces
At least.
That leaves three pieces for
One really brilliant mate
And you're only supposed to have
One really brilliant mate anyway.

I'm worrying all over again.
It could be the start
Of a nervous countdown.
Twenty-one never was an
Easy number to divide.
Twenty-four is so much easier.
It can be broken up
Into threes, eights, twelves, twos, sixes and
Fours

Therefore I think it would be correct
For me to keep the whole bar.

Then I eat all of it
In six mouthfuls
Four pieces per mouthful
One after another, after another, after another
Right now this is the first time
I've felt quite so sick
In my entire life.

You know what?
I shouldn't have done it.
But it *was* a good exercise in sums,
Wasn't it?

Badly equipped

Teacher's report, Monday morning.
Situation – hopeless.
Class – utterly useless.

        Us pupils we've lost our rulers.
Teacher: Now let's get this straight.
        And our rubbers.
Teacher: I've erased the thought from my head.
        We can't find our pencils either.
Teacher: And let's be blunt about it.
        Nor our writing pens.
Teacher: I'm lost for words.
        Even our memories have gone astray.
Teacher: Let's just forget about it
        And start all over
        Again.

The Poet who painted his Toenails red

Today we have a visitor
A special treat worth waiting for.
Now authors have a certain style
A friendly face and kindly smile.
Miss, will he be wearing a suit?
Oh no my dear, it doesn't suit.
Surely then a shirt and tie?
My dear it's not the author's style.

Let us welcome our visitor
A truly brilliant author.
You'll know him from the creative look
He's dreaming up tales for another new book.
Miss, will he be wearing a beard?
Maybe, but they're not all hippies, my dear.
Miss, will he be sporting glasses?
I'd say there is every chance, yes.

Miss, will he be acting strange?
Will he float above the ground?
Does he have a family
Or do writers live alone?

In sheds, on beaches, in deep dark woods
With fairies and elves to edit his books,
In cafes and car-parks, on lonely street corners
Where no one disturbs him when he's writing
poems.

Today we had a visitor
It was a treat worth waiting for.
He wore a happy face
And a sad one sometimes.
You could tell by the look in his voice
He liked to write poems.
The words he spoke reminded me
Of something deep inside
Which loves the words
That people write –
And I didn't mind

Him painting his toenails red
And wearing a long flowing lady's dress –
Oh and not forgetting the beard,
Of course.

Writing can be hard Work

Perfect!
I'd like you to write
Your own story –
The opening bit.
Any questions?
Please, what's the date?
And the heading?
Can we draw a picture?
Which way round do we put the paper?
Which way round does the writing go?
No, no, no, no, no, no, no!
Forget the heading,
The paper, pencil, date,
Just get on and write!
Tut, tut, tut, tut, tut, tut, tut.
Alright, alright, alright, alright!
Children shaking heads reply
The minutes pass, the pencils tap
The eyes are glazed, the page is blank
All thirty pupils have that look –
We're ready now but please –
We're stuck.

When I am away (for all my children)

Your form misshapen, uncertain size
Floats across my scaled eyes
Playing tricks upon my mind
You in misty corners hide
Elusive with your faded smile
Stolen by another child
And, try as hard as I might try
I'm missing by a thousand miles.
A growing emptiness inside
Heavy weight of wasted time
Suspended till a turning tide
Brings me gasping back to life.

Stealing close to see you sleep
I realise my distant dream
To touch the real, bone and skin
To make myself a whole again.

The Real World

My imagination is a
Window on another world.
I leave it wide open
So that when I draw back the curtain
I cannot possibly be certain
Of what it is that's lurking
Save I know it will be interesting
And its story never ending.

I can wish what I want
I can turn it on or off.
I can follow it as far as I like
To the ends of my brain
And all the way back home again.
It is a land made for explorers
For people who are fed up
Of all those others.

Some people I know
Close their window.
They say they like
To live in this world
And that only babies
Make up stories
About elves and fairies

And that people with imagination
Have lost touch with reality.
But what do they know
If they've never opened that window?
Climbed down and
Looked back through
To the land that lies
On the other side
Of this very, very thin
Glassy divide.

First Day

Her eyes it seems
Are swimming in tears as
She struggles with heartstrings
Tuned to the deepest fears
She surely feels.
His hot hand clings to hers
A tiny face explains
I don't know, I'm not certain,
Cross his heart, he draws a curtain,
Alas for her a see-through one.
He is a brave boy
A big boy does not cry
But checks for the mood
In his mother's eye
Who turns to make
Her sad face smile.
She will not cry
One last good-bye.

He carries the cooling hand
Lifting makes a limp wave.
In the harbour he spies her
Flag hands fluttering
I love, love, love you darling.
A wind of change blows him

A turning tide sends him
Sailing into a classroom
- His island home,
A refuge from the stormy sea –
Whilst she, head sunk in empty buggy
Steers a course through clouds of mums
She runs, she runs, she runs, she runs.

Smoothes her senses though restless sees
Everyone else so why not me?
But that heart moves the clock hands
Onward, onward relentlessly.

Time

I think we should do
Something about the problem
Of people wasting time.
They just throw it away
Together will any old rubbish
And instantly forget about it.
They should take their time
Down to the recycling centre
Where someone could make
All the seconds and minutes
And hours and days and
Weeks and years
Into time capsules
To give away to poor people,
Short-of-time people
Who would then be
Able to live longer.

That's not as bad
As killing time.
People do that when
They're standing there
Waiting for something to happen –
People in bus queues
And doctor's surgeries

Are always doing it.
I don't know what time
Did wrong to deserve it.
Maybe one day we will
Have killed all the time
And there won't be any
Left for anyone to use
Wisely or otherwisely.

Then we'll all have to
Make time for something
If we want to do it badly enough.

I think it's high time
We stopped wasting and killing
And trying to make time
And instead cherished
Every little moment
In our life
Time.

Barcelona vs. Manchester United

The Catalan cat
Drags his scrawny body
Down the sunlit streets
Delving for the shadowy
Home of his kind,
Only smiling when his
Team are winning,
The rest of the time
Down in the mouth
Grim, too thin –
He needs feeding.
In contrast to our Cheshire cat
Good-humoured, friendly
Fat and grinning
And confident that next season
Marks for his team, Manchester United,
A brand new beginning.

*This poem was written one week after Barcelona won the
Champions' League Cup, defeating Manchester United in
the final. I was in Barcelona!

Penalty-taker

Will it die
Or will the game come alive?
Will there ever
Be an extra time?
Hushed,
Head in hands
Not daring to watch the man
In whose boots
Hides the terrible truth,
Who carries with him
The hopes and dreams
Of a packed stadium.
(Hey not much pressure, then).
In purgatory they await him
And his angel spell
Which floats the ball
To the back of the net.
His heavenly spot kick
Redeems the game
So that every soul
Is free again
And every heart that stopped
Beats one and the same
And red blood pulses
Through the cup tie's veins.

Super Striker slays Gloomy Goalie

We have a striker
I'm called Super
I score all the goals
So I'm the one who's popular.

I'm selfish, I'm greedy
I never pass the ball
I never think about the team
I go it all alone.

I hang around the goalmouth
Chatting at their goalie
I tell him, "Hey I'm Super
Yeah everybody knows me."

And in my dreams they hug and kiss
They tell me, "Brilliant, Super!"
But when I wake I'm sure to find
I'm lonely Goalie Gloomy

Who shuffles awkward on the line
Scared stiff by their attack
Who'd like to crawl inside the net
But there's no turning back.

Their striker shoots to slay
To cut me down to size
Gloomy in this goalmouth
I wilt before his eyes.

I tell myself that it's not real
I'll pinch myself to see
That I'm gloomy muddy goalie
And winning's just a dream.

Plasters

Never, never trust an adult
With a plaster –
Here's the picture:
You've grazed your knee
On the worst gravel ever
Since you fell off your bike
Taking the corner.
And now you're trying your bestest
Not to let it bother,
Yes you're trying your hardest
To avoid – the
Plaster!
Still they have you plastered
And you keep screaming – No!
Every time they want
To take the thing off you –
Because plasters sting
Like anything.
Like anything
A plaster stings.

So when they say
'Here, just a peek,"
Beware that adults
Like to sneak
Up on you and –
Rip it off!
'There we are, that didn't hurt?'
And all you can blubber
As you try to recover is
'Yes!'

Only a Game

Dad's a football referee
You'd think he'd give it
A rest on Sunday
But no, out with his family
(For a stroll down our street)
He's looking to see
Where we're putting our feet.
'All in a line now.
All in a line
No one wants to
Be caught offside.'

And when we complain
Say 'Dad we're just shopping.'
He says 'I'm the ref
And you stop your arguing.'
Mum she tackles him –
Over the top.
Dad says he really
Has had enough.
Shows her the red card
Her head bowed in shame
But Mum don't you know
That it's only a game?

Watersliding for Professionals

Exciting and exhilarating
Successful watersliding
Is all about descending,
On bare skin gliding,
From the top to
The bottom as
Fast as one can
And, keeping one's resistance low
Make sure one's trunks are down
And thus baring one's bottom
One turns round and round
And rest assured the rest
Of one will spiral to the ground.

Cool Dip

Refined and empty the pool said nothing.
Its bottom was clean and its top was shining
And in between was all clear calm
I had to jump in it –
This looking-glass balm
Which broke into a thousand pieces
I jumped clean out
And stood there freezing.
I observed the shattered
Remains of my dream –
How pools aren't always
As good as they seem.

My Dad's bigger than yours

Ner, ner, ner, ner, ner!
My Dad's bigger than yours
My Mum's bigger than yours
My brother's bigger than yours
My sister's bigger than yours
My dog's bigger than yours
My cat's bigger than yours

So what!
All of mine have got guns
And none of them wear glasses.

Beards

I've always been scared of beards
But the other day I was really scared
When I was looking very hard
Trying to guess what lived in it
And if the creature from the
Beard ever ventured out
When to my horror, I was to discover
The beard spoke – with a mouth.

Fooling God

All dead animals live in the sky
Above where planes to Mallorca fly.
Shall we, shall we go to that place
And meet with God in his Heavenly base?
Up there is where God stays,
Flying you can catch a glimpse of his face.

Here on earth the animals are alive
And won't see God until they die
And it's the same for children, mums and dads,
Aunties, uncles, grandpas, nans.
But I'll trick God, I have a plan:

Tonight after tea instead of our bed
We'll lie down in the grass
And pretend to be dead.
Daddy don't worry – we won't be cold
Snuggle up to me and we'll be brave and bold.
I'll hold your hand and tell you some stories
There's no such thing as ghosties and ghoulies.
Don't worry Daddy do just like me
Stay very, very still like this – see.
Then we'll wait and very soon
God will come down from his home near the moon.
He'll be sad and sorry for us

Coming close he'll give us a kiss
And carry us on through the sky
Above where planes to Mallorca fly.
He'll think that we are dead and gone
But up in Heaven we'll prove him wrong.
Fooled you, God! We're not dead
Me and Dad we joked instead
And God he'll smile and get the joke
And disappear in a puff of smoke.

We'll fall down to the earth below
Back to our garden – no one will know
That we've see our God face to face
And all those dead animals floating in space.

Fishing for the Truth

My mum went fishing for the truth
With a long, long line
And a very big hook on the end of it.
I hid the truth and dragged it down
With me as I dived to the muddy bottom
And sank in the dark
Of the deep, well hidden.
And there I stayed, lying

Down and scared stiff of being caught
But, I thought
If I stayed there in that silent water
She might give up
And go fishing for the truth somewhere else
But she knew she was on to a good catch

And her rod remained perched,
The line dangling now, searching.
I couldn't remain in
This underworld forever
She wouldn't have to wait
Too much longer.

She cast out further
Threw more bait over
'Honesty is the best policy'
I heard her murmur.
I couldn't resist it
I floated on up
To the surface.

I felt the light warmth of her motherly hug
She told me it was a bad thing I had done
But on owning up – I was ready to swim.

The Lady and the Dog

Perched in the basket
On the front of a bicycle
He dons a smile
But his owner
Seat bound
Wears a weary frown.
I wonder if things
Were the other way round
Would the dog be grinning
Having to do all that cycling?
And would the lady
Free from all responsibility
And with her bottom
Encased in a basket of straw,
Wear the expression of one
Who could never want for more?

Ice Cubes

If you go to very cold places
You can still find glaciers
Which are good for climbing on
And putting in glasses of
Drink to keep them cold
Even though you wouldn't want to
Because it's not very warm outside.

Nowadays we use fridges instead
Since most of the glaciers melted
After the last ice age
A long long time ago
When some fool
Unplugged all those freezers.

Make up your Mind

Right.
Let's start with the adults.
Tea or coffee?
I can't make up my mind.
Coffee or tea.
Do you know, I'm not sure.
Black or white?
Now you're asking.
Sugar or none?
Hmmm well – do you think it needs it?
Cup or mug?
The cups – are they big or small?
Biscuit?
Well I shouldn't but maybe...

And how about the children – ice creams?
Yeaaah! White with
        Five flakes
        Loads of chocolate sauce
        Massive cornet
        Give it to me
        Now!

Dressing up

I was bored
So I put the TV
And computer on.
I looked quite different
In my electronic outfit.
People watched me
Everywhere I went –
Quite a sensation
With wide screen
And high definition
Graphics package
In high resolution –
But it just wasn't me
I couldn't think
Independently,
Someone had to programme me.
So I took off
The computer and TV
And instead, picked up a book
And with my head stuck
Between the pages
Looked quite good.

Nod and Don

In the land of Nod
Both day and night
People are never
Seen upright.
Always sleeping
They spend their
Life dreaming
Of living in the land of Don
Where people never lie down.
Always busy they spend their
Lives active and wish they could live
In the land of Nod
But instead they have to try
To sleep standing up.

Dog and God

God is dog
Spelt backwards
And I do believe
Mine came straight from Heaven
His four paws upon this
Earth serene treading.
His canine smile
Lessens any load,
The angels wove those ears
So soft to the stroke
And wagged the tail on him
That tells me I'm never alone,
Louder than any human can.
Me and him out walking,
I'm not in the real world -
It's a painting
And all the things that are frightening
Are quickly fading
And there's just him and me.
Everything is changing
Into a wilderness
A world of furry kindness
Where dog is God
Spelt backwards.

Ghost Train

The screeching of the ghost train
A slow and chokey start
Bright silver wheels gleaming
In the winter's evening dark.
Black curtains at the window
Dare you take a peep?
But the carriages are empty
Or so... it... would...seem.
They're picking up a little steam
Billowing clouds of smoke
I watch from the embankment
At the shape that shovels coal.
Strange shadow in the red light
Hunched back of fireman
Who feeds the hungry engine
So the ghost train rattles on.
Rattles on and on and on
Faster, faster still
I see the ghost train rushing by
From the old abandoned bridge.
Sparks they are a-shooting
In the settled white of night
The whistle sounds a mourning cry
As the ghost train flashes by
And on to the last station

Crunch and scrape of brake,
Nervous are the carriages
They shiver and they shake
And then an eerie silence
I wait and wait and wait,
At last the click of carriage door
I want to run – too late!

Out come the ghosts
I hide inside the mist
I watch them through the station
Across the lonely street.
Up the hill they falter
Soul mates in a line
Their spirits tired, double bent
They know it is their time.
They turn into the churchyard
Through the creaking gate
Each one to a gravestone
Each one stops to pray.
Then all at once they fall
And sink into the ground
Into their watching grave
They pass without a sound.

Come and ride the ghost train
Special midnight trip
Visit all your favourite haunts
Before you rest in peace.

Oh! Tea! (Nana's rap)

Don't need MacDonald's don't need Kentucky
'Ere in the kitchen I'm strikin' it lucky
Pouring the cupfuls of muddy brown liquid
Livin' it large with a mugful hey innit?

> *Tea, tea, a lovely cup of tea*
> *There's nothing more exciting*
> *In the world you see.*
> *Tea, tea, just give it to me*
> *There's nothing more exciting*
> *Than a nice cup of tea.*

Don't want to play games, don't want to do
football
Want to drink tea with me friends down the
church hall
Don't need computer, don't need the Ipod
Just want me kettle, just want me T-pot.

> *Tea, tea, a lovely cup of tea*
> *There's nothing more exciting*
> *In the world you see.*
> *Tea, tea, just give it to me*
> *There's nothing more exciting*
> *Than a nice cup of tea.*

Don't want to drama, don't want to dance
I'm watching me water brew up those tea bags
Watching the flavour come flooding on through
Sitting there making a wonderful brew.

Tea, tea, a lovely cup of tea
There's nothing more exciting
In the world you see.
Tea, tea, just give it to me
There's nothing more exciting
Than a nice cup of tea.

You children who is needing respect
Put down your coke and drink tea instead
Come and live life with your nana's flavour
It's tea that you savour, yeah do us a favour!

Tea, tea, a lovely cup of tea
There's nothing more exciting
In the world you see.
Tea, tea, just give it to me
There's nothing more exciting
Than a nice cup of tea.

Pedestrians, where are you?

There's no room for you pedestrians no more
There's no room for you pedestrians no more
It's all ten tonne trucks
You're out of luck
You're gonna have to leave here
There's no room for you pedestrians no more.

Just try to walk
Well it's a joke
If the cars miss you
You'll choke on smoke
Your bike's not safe
That bus don't come
Get in your car
Like everyone.

There's no room for you pedestrians no more
There's no room for you pedestrians no more
It's all ten tonne trucks
You're out of luck
You're gonna have to leave here
There's no room for you pedestrians no more.

Peg your nose
Plug your ears

Pray to God
And close your eyes.
Look out!
Train is derailed
The old tram gone
The car is king
The queue is long
The pavement's gone
The road's sure wide
No room to walk
No place to hide.

You know what?
We need a revolution
A kind of transport evolution
It's the only possible solution!

Gotta have room for us pedestrians right now
Gotta have room for us pedestrians right now
If you want a future
And gridlock doesn't suit yer
Gotta have room for us pedestrians, on yeah!
Gotta have room for us pedestrians right now
Gotta have room for us pedestrians right now
If you want a future
And gridlock doesn't suit yer
Gotta have room for us pedestrians, on yeah!

Sock Fluff

Derived from the modern English, 'sock'
And 'fluff', as in 'fluffy sock'.
The phenomenon is a recent one
Consistent with the habit
Of putting the foot in a sock
Especially of the type likely to yield fluff.
Unknown in ancient times
As Egyptian, Roman and Greek peoples
Were restricted to either bare feet or sandals.
Not to be confused with 'cheese'
Also found between the toes.
The former has a particularly bad odour
Whereas sock fluff is noticeably without scent
And indeed harmless except those
Isolated cases of 'fluffy foot'
Where fluff stuffed gaps between toes close.
This is due entirely to excess deposits
From poor quality so-called 'shedders'
Which may be easily removed by a kind
Friend or neighbour's fingernail thus
Ridding the problem without surgical intervention.

The Return of the Chocolate Biscuit

Here come the chocolate biscuits
They sweep across the land
"Freedom for the biscuit!"
So cry the marching band.
We will never give in
Though some of us be eaten!
Their leader cries, "Onward you guys
We'll never be defeated!"
Oh yes, how long we've suffered
Nibbled crunch-ed too
Others drowned in boiling tea
Before they swallow you!
For every one that's eaten
Another will replace him.
We'll breed and breed a little more
Yes we will overcome them!

The humans and their ugly mouths
The teeth that crush and bite
The greedy eyes, the selfish smile
No pity for our plight.
But now we're off to London
The palace of Buckingham!
An audience with Her Majesty
We'll put it to her – Ma'am

We're sorry to disturb you
A crisis it at hand
We've marched upon your palace
From right across your lands.

Your Majesty - an amnesty!
The chocolate biscuit must be free!
Leave us alone and let us be
Your Majesty, your Majesty.

I see, I see
'Tis truly sad
That we should choose to eat you.
Suppose we swear to give it up
The Prince and corgis too?
No tit-bits in the palace
No murder in this place!
A refuge for the biscuit
A secret hiding place.

Now the doggies love their little snack
And the Prince, 'Oh yes, me too!'
But alas! We can't go on like this
We must look after you.

So then I'll tell my people
Yes I shall make it law,

May God forgive you sinners
But don't eat biscuits any more.
Our chocolate friends
Have had enough!
'I quite agree!'
And the corgis – 'Woof!'

Yes, yes, yes, I'm with you
I'm the Prince
Now listen do!
Don't crunch or munch
Or gnaw or chew
Follow our example
Too!

I declare the chocolate biscuit
A protected species
And so my loyal subjects
You must never eat him.
And should you do so, I must warn
You'll suffer as they do
The Prince and I will just stand by
Whilst the corgis dine on you.

Poet's Revenge

One afternoon I made up this poem
All completely out of nothing.
It was the type of poem
People would laugh at
Because they understood what
I was going on about.
I can't remember – it might
Have been best sung
But in the whole poem world
I reckon it was the best one.
Now, I thought I'd locked it up in my memory,
I thought I'd finished it properly.

When I tried to think about my
Poem I found I couldn't.
I looked but it wasn't in a book.
It wasn't under my pillow
Or written on the back of a hand.
Someone had stolen my poem!
Whilst I was sleeping
Someone had come creeping
And taken it from my brain
And for evermore they'd be saying –
'Oh and did you know?
This is _**MY**_ poem

That I made up from nothing.
You'll laugh at it
Because you understand it –
And it might have a tune.'
That's what they'd say
In their know-all way
To the whole world listening
To this thief with his
Prize poem glittering –
And he'd be up there
On the stage twittering
And he's just about
To start at the beginning
When open-mouthed
He admits to the crowd
'I can't remember a thinging.'

If you've enjoyed this, take a look at the website for other children's books by the same author:
www.InspireToWrite.co.uk